P9-DVG-599

D1132803

Interpreting in
MEDICAL SETTINGS

Interpreting in MEDICAL SETTINGS

Carol J. Patrie

Interpreting in Medical Settings

Printed and Manufactured in the United States of America.
Published by DawnSignPress.

ISBN: 1-58121-065-5

For information, please contact:

DawnSignPress

6130 Nancy Ridge Drive
San Diego, CA 92121
858-625-0600 V/TTY 858-625-2336 FAX
ORDER TOLL FREE 1-800-549-5350
VISIT US AT www.dawnsign.com

Table of Contents

Also Available

Interpreting in Insurance Settings

Interpreting in Legal Settings

Acknowledgments

The idea for Interpreting Settings originated in 1995 and has been carefully developed in the intervening years. It is a special treat for me to thank all of the talented people who have assisted in making my vision become reality during this time.

At DawnSignPress a small number of people pull off a myriad of production and publishing miracles on a daily basis. I thank Dan Veltri and Joseph Josselyn for their wonderful work in editing the videos and Yoon Lee for filming them. Thanks also must go to each of the people who so graciously agreed to be filmed so that many others could get a realistic feel for the dynamics of an interpreted event.

Rebecca Ryan has worked with me on this project with remarkable clarity and focus. I am especially thankful for her encouragement and optimism in all phases of our work together. Any project that is overseen by Rebecca is deeply enriched by her valuable insights and any author that has the good fortune to work with her becomes a better author.

I am continually grateful for Joe Dannis's generosity of spirit and his conviction in my work. I feel incredibly lucky to be associated with DawnSignPress and its staff.

Interpreting in MEDICAL SETTINGS

THE GOAL AND RATIONALE

In interpreter education, it is important to observe situations where interpretation takes place before actually performing the interpretations. *Interpreting in Medical Settings* allows you to learn about aspects of interpreting dialogues by observing dialogic interpreting in medical settings. The video and book promote observational learning and provide exposure to relevant terminology.

THE POWER OF OBSERVATIONAL LEARNING

There are two main ways to learn new responses: one is by direct experience and the other is by observation of "models," meaning persons who are more experienced in rendering interpretations. According to Bandura (1977) virtually all learning that results from direct experience occurs on a vicarious basis by first observing other people's behavior and then later performing the behavior. Remembering how the model performed the behavior helps you formulate your own response without having to go through trial and error.

Bandura explains that observational learning can shorten the time it takes to acquire skills. "Rarely do people learn behaviors under natural conditions that they have never seen performed by others" (p. 22). For example, aspiring surgeons must observe many hours of procedures performed by experienced surgeons before performing surgery themselves. If people learned only through trial and error, the amount of time needed to learn is increased, and the consequences could be negative. Interpretation is a complex process and the consequences of a faulty interpretation could negatively affect those who are relying on the interpretation, so it is clear that observation must play an important role in interpreter education. The more costly and hazardous the effects of the potential errors, the greater the need for observing competent examples.

Even though many interpreter education programs want students to observe a wide variety of settings, these are often difficult to arrange, especially in restricted settings where the deaf client divulges personal information. This video allows students, their teachers, and interpreters to observe interpreted interaction without interfering with the dialogue or the interpretation.

The acquisition of linguistic skill is another area where observing competent models aids in the learning process. Children do not learn language in a random pattern; instead, they learn by listening to language and then formulating their own utterances. Learning to interpret is not random either. This learning process occurs in an orderly fashion. First, fluency in two languages is required. Then intralingual or single language skills must be strengthened, followed by exercises in interlingual skill development, such as translation, consecutive interpreting, and simultaneous interpreting. Watching an interpreter at work allows the observer to develop ideas about which interpretations and decisions are most effective within a given setting.

THE FOUR COMPONENTS OF OBSERVATIONAL LEARNING

Bandura suggests that observational learning has four main components: paying attention, retaining information, reproducing observed behaviors, and incorporating new skills. These are briefly described below.

Paying Attention

In order learn by observation, a person must attend to and accurately perceive the behavior. "The rate and level of observational learning is also partially determined by the nature of the modeled behaviors themselves, their salience and complexity. In addition, observers' capacities to process information govern how much they will benefit from observed experiences. People's perceptual sets, deriving from past experience and situational requirements, affect what features they extract from observations and how they interpret what they see and hear." (p. 25). This means that you may obtain more information in your second or third observation of the same conversation because the observation process itself allows you to learn and create a base of information on which you can build.

Retaining Information

You must remember what you observe in order to be influenced by what you observe. You must be able to remember it long after the model is no longer present. The memory of the observation is saved symbolically. Humans have an advanced capacity for symbolization that promotes learning by observation. Observational learning depends on two representational systems that allow you to access the symbolic memory. Bandura calls these two systems imaginal and verbal. Imaginal retention means that some behavior is retained as an *image* of a performance. Exposure to visually observable events, objects, and people creates an image in memory that can be retrieved after the actual objects are no longer present. Visual imagery plays an important role in observational learning.

The other way that symbols are created is through verbal coding. By "verbal coding" Bandura does not necessarily mean acoustic coding. Instead, the concept that underlies his theory is that linguistic shorthand is stored in memory. Bandura's theory does not address sign language directly but may be extended to include it by acknowledging that American Sign Language is a set of symbols just as English is a set of symbols. In either case, symbolic codes, such as languages, carry a great deal of information in forms that are easy to store and retrieve. Information that is presented in ASL or English is coded as linguistic input and stored. "Details of the route traveled by a model, for example, can be acquired, retained and later reproduced more accurately by converting the visual information into a verbal code describing a series of right and left turns as RLRRL than by relying on visual imagery of the route" (p. 26). If the directions were presented in ASL, the information might be coded as a series of signs indicating right and left. When modeled activities are transformed into images or linguistic symbols, they are readily usable and become memory codes for performance. Observers who code modeled activities retain behaviors better than observers who do not code the information.

Mental rehearsal is another important aspect of retaining information. Mentally rehearsing a modeled response increases the likelihood of remembering the behavior. When lack of opportunity prevents overt practice, it is even more important to rehearse mentally and visualize yourself performing the activity. Bandura stresses that mental rehearsal in which individuals visualize themselves performing the appropriate behavior increases proficiency and retention. "The highest level of observational learning is achieved by first organizing and rehearsing the modeled behavior symbolically and then enacting it overtly" (Bandura & Jeffery, 1973, p. 27).

Bandura and others (1973) conducted experiments to determine the effect of symbolic coding on observational learning. They found that symbolic coding in observational learning, whether the coding is images or linguistic input, is important for adult learners. When observers talk about observed behaviors or observe modeled behaviors more than once, they retain behaviors better than those who simply observe or are distracted during observation.

Reproducing Observed Information

According to Bandura (1977) the third component of modeling focuses on changing symbolic representations into appropriate action. Skills cannot be perfected through observation alone, they must be practiced and improved through a series of adjustments to the performance. The four aspects of this component of observational learning are cognitive organization of responses, their initiation, their monitoring, and their refinement on the basis of informative feedback. For example, when learning to interpret, after you have observed an interpretation, you must first organize your cognitive response ("Yes, that was an interpretation that I would like to study and perform") and then initiate or perform the interpretation yourself. Next, you receive feedback from someone who has monitored or observed your interpretation. Based on that feedback you can refine or modify your interpretation in your next attempt to interpret the same or similar material.

Incorporating New Skills

Bandura (1977) says that there are two main reasons that people will be motivated to adopt behaviors they observe. First, observers are more likely to adopt modeled behavior if it results in outcomes they value. Second, they are more likely to want to adopt behaviors that appear to be effective for others.

Whether you realize it or not, you are evaluating each interpretation that you observe and perform, so you will most likely want to repeat only those that you feel were successful. This means that if you observe a model that is, in your opinion, excellent and effective, you will be highly motivated to attend to, remember, and try to reproduce a similar interpretation. If the observed interpreter's skills are very advanced and if you are a beginner, it is likely that you may miss some of the salient features, that you may not remember all the features, and that you may not yet have the motor skills to render a similar interpretation. However, by repeated observations of the same interpretation, you increase your attention and memory. Repeated attempts to render the interpretation improve your accuracy in using the necessary motor skills.

The four components of observational learning will be at work as you watch this video and practice interpretations. You will be viewing images of interpretations that will build up your imaginal stores of information. Through discussion you will linguistically code what you have seen. This will help you remember what you have observed and will make observational learning more effective.

PHASES OF THE INTERPRETATION PROCESS

The sections that follow emphasize the salient features of interpretation so that you can apply the components of observational learning to the interpreting process. The most critical awareness you can develop is noticing how errors in interpretation affect communication. The severity of errors can correlate to the phase in which they occur in the interpretation process. The phases where errors can occur, and the possible consequences, are briefly described here. Remember that interpretation is not really a linear process, as all parts of the interpretation process affect each other. In studying interpretation, however, it is convenient to discuss the process in three separate phases—comprehension, transfer, and reformulation—in order to notice the effects of the interpreter's decisions. The following is based on Gile's (1995) sequential model of translation. For a more complete explanation of his sequential model of translation and effort model of interpretation, see *Basic Concepts in Interpreter and Translator Training.*

Comprehension

Comprehension is the first phase of the interpreting process. It includes fully analyzing the message, including fingerspelled words when the message is in ASL. Errors in comprehension are very serious and may prevent the interpreter from successfully moving on to later phases of the interpreting process. If the interpreter has misunderstood the message or failed to comprehend, it is not possible to convey the source language message accurately in the target language. The effect of miscomprehension will depend on the context, the situation and the participants. Those who depend on the interpretation usually do not realize when the interpreter has misunderstood or failed to comprehend the source message and generally assume that the interpretation is faithful and accurate in all respects. When the interpreter has misunderstood or failed to comprehend the source message, the result is likely to be that the participants who are depending on the interpretation will misunderstand each other.

Transfer

Transfer is the phase in which the interpreter mentally formulates an interpretation in the target language and envisions how the interpretation should be rendered into the target language syntax. Sometimes the interpreter has correctly understood the message but does not know how to transfer the message into the target language. This can happen when there are weaknesses in either syntax or vocabulary in the target language. Errors in this phase are less severe than those in the comprehension phase because the interpreter has understood the message well enough to begin the interpretation process. Errors during the transfer phase are more severe than errors that occur afterward, however, because the accuracy of each remaining phase depends on the accuracy of the earlier phases in the process. The message cannot be reformulated if the interpreter does not know how to transfer it.

Difficulty in the transfer phase may cause the interpreter to render a message in the target language that follows the source language syntax. Another type of error that can surface during transfer is choosing incorrect lexical items in the target language. When either of these types of errors occurs, the person receiving the interpretation must work harder to make sense out of the interpretation, may misunderstand, or may obtain no sense from the message at all. When errors occur during the transfer phase, it is likely that the participants in the dialogue will misunderstand each other, or worse, think that they understand each other when they really do not.

Reformulation

Reformulation is the visible result of the previous phases in the interpretation process. In this phase the interpreter renders the message into the target language. It is possible for the interpreter to correctly understand the message, correctly transfer the message, and still encounter problems in reformulation. Errors in reformulation may include mispronunciations, awkward sentence constructions, and other errors that are generally much less serious than errors that may occur in the previous two phases. When errors occur in this phase, the recipient of the interpretation can usually make sense out of the message, but the message will still be skewed to some extent by these errors. Ideally, the Interpreter renders the interpretation in a manner that is appropriate to the form of the target language and preserves the meaning of the source message.

Error Taxonomy

One of the most useful ways to categorize errors is to study the impact of the error on communication. Not all errors are equally serious. In order to determine how serious an error is you may use an error taxonomy to help sort out the effect of the error on the message. For example, some omissions may be intentional, such as leaving out a detail in order to maintain the integrity of the overall message while working to keep up with a rapid speaker. Sometimes a misinterpretation may not have a noticeable effect on the communication, especially when the people in the conversation have sufficient background information.

Here is one way to organize the seriousness of errors in interpretation (Gorman, 1989):

Very serious	Total skew of the message due to comprehension problems;
Quite serious	Total skew of the message due to following L1 syntax;
Somewhat serious	Minor skew of the message due to omission or addition of detail;
Not serious	Error does not skew the message; and
No errors	Communicative function is well preserved.

THE ARRANGEMENT FOR *Interpreting in Medical Settings*

Various professionals who provide specific services to the community were contacted to see if they would like to participate in the observations project. The professional service providers in the series include attorneys, an insurance agent, medical doctors, and a dentist.

Interpreters were also asked if they would like to be involved in the project. The interpreters selected did not have deaf parents and, for the most part, learned sign language as adults. Some were certified interpreters and some were not. These interpreters were chosen to represent naturalistic samples of what really happens in interpreted dialogues.

Deaf people were invited to participate in the project. They were not given scripts and the scenes were not rehearsed. Each person on the tape introduced himself or herself to the viewing audience but not to each other on camera. There were two cameras, one that filmed the interpreter and the hearing person and one that filmed the deaf person. Due to the placement constraints imposed by filming, the interpreters did not have a choice in selecting or arranging seating positions. Although not scripted or rehearsed, the scenarios were arranged to permit a natural flow of conversation.

Possible Uses for This Tape

The primary use for this tape is for observing interpretations in medical settings. Each observation depicts a medical professional and a deaf person seeking medical attention. Teachers can guide students in discussions before the observations by noting which aspects of the interpretation should receive attention. Discussions after observing the interpretations can be helpful and are sure to generate many questions about interpreting in such settings. Study groups can use the videos as discussion material, and mentors can use the videos to generate discussions and to develop strategies for interpreting interaction. When discussing these observations, it is important to remember that the focus is not on criticism of the interpreters, but rather on the effect the interpreter's choices had on the communication.

This book provides ways to draw your attention to important dynamics of the interpreted dialogues, strategies for interactive interpreting, and discussion topics. For additional information on interpreting dialogic events see *Sign Language Interpreting: Deconstructing the Myth of Neutrality* (2000) by Melanie Metzger, and *Interpreting as Interaction* (1992) by Cecilia Wadensjo.

Suggested Directions

Before watching a dialogue or "setting," go to the list of terms that appear just prior to the transcript for each dialogue. You should know what these terms mean before watching the dialogue in order to maximize your observation experience. You can discuss these terms in a group or work on them individually. The transcript for each dialogue is included in this booklet as a valuable study tool.

The utterances marked "Interpreter" depict the interpretation and are not a gloss or a translation of the ASL utterance. These are the interpreter's words and so are attributed to the interpreter, not to the deaf person. You can use the transcript of the interpretations to compare the interpretation with the ASL source message on the videotape. You can also compare the English source message with the ASL interpretation on the videotape.

Although the primary purpose of this tape is for observing interpreters at work, you may wish to practice rendering your own interpretations of the material. You can study the printed versions of the spoken English when you are ready to render your own interpretations.

Here are some other ways you can improve your awareness of the dynamics in an interpreted situation:

1. Notice the effect of physical placement of the interpreter in the setting.
2. Notice to what extent the interpreter manages the interaction. For example, sometimes the interpreter may need to ask for clarification and repetition. What is the effect?
3. Notice the effect of incorrect interpretations on responses from the other participants.
4. Notice the effect of comprehension errors on the part of the interpreter.
5. Notice the effect of comprehension errors on the part of either the physician or the deaf client.
6. Notice the importance of interpreting a yes/no question carefully.
7. Notice the effect of processing time on the effectiveness of the interpretation. When the interpreter allows enough time to comprehend the message fully, errors are less likely.
8. Notice whether or not the emotional affects of the source and target messages match.

9. Notice strategies used for requesting clarification.

10. Notice how the interpreter indicates who is talking, especially at the beginning of a conversation where the use of the word "my" could be confusing to the deaf client.

11. Notice what happens when the question is not what the client is expecting.

Discussion Starters

1. How would you prepare for an interpreting assignment with an ear, nose and throat specialist or a dentist?

2. If you had the opportunity to have a pre-assignment meeting with each of the parties, what questions would you ask to help you interpret more effectively?

3. What would you wear to interpret in an medical setting?

4. "Adjacency pairs" are two part sequences that occur in conversations, as in greetings (e.g., in English "Hello" is followed by the response "Hello," and "How are you?" by "Fine") (Metzger, 2000). Look for three adjacency pairs and discuss how you would interpret them.

5. When two people speak at the same time, their utterances are said to "overlap," and the inter-

preter must decide how to handle the situation. There are three ways to handle overlap of adjacency pairs (Roy, 1989, 1993):

a. Controlling the floor,

b. Retaining part of the message for later, and

c. Ignoring the overlap and interpreting neither of the utterances. Look for examples of these three ways to handle overlap and discuss the effectiveness of each.

6. According to Zimmer (1989) interpreters "fill" silences with repetitions as a result of discomfort with silence: "If the repetitions or other fillers were initiated by the interpreter and not the other participants, the fillers can change the impact of the original sentences and the perceptions that the participants have of each other." Look for examples of fillers and discuss their impact on the communication.

7. What is the purpose of the interaction? Is the purpose met?

8. Find two passages where you admire the way in which the interpreter conveyed the message and practice those. Stop the tape after each utterance if you need more time or would like to practice simultaneous interpreting. Alternatively, you can let the tape play and render your own interpretation of the conversation. It is best to videotape your work to analyze later.

9. Find two passages where you feel the message was skewed and render your own version of an interpretation.

10. How do you indicate when someone is speaking directly to the interpreter?

11. Develop strategies for the interpreter to respond to the hearing person in the context of an interpreted situation—speak only, sign only, or sign and speak at the same time. What is the advisability of each?

REFERENCES

Bandura, A., and Jeffrey, R.W. (1973) "Role of Symbolic Coding and Rehearsal Processes in Observational Learning." *Journal of Personality and Social Psychology,* 26, 122–130.

Bandura, A. (1977). *Social learning theory.* Englewood Cliffs, NJ: Prentice-Hall.

Gile, D. (1995). *Basic concepts and models for interpreter and translator training.* Philadelphia, PA: John Benjamins.

Gorman, D. (1989). *Personal communication.*

Metzger, M. (2000). *Sign Language interpreting: Deconstructing the myth of neutrality.* Washington, DC: Gallaudet University Press.

Roy, C. (1989) A sociolinguistic analysis of the interpreter's role in the turn exchanges of an interpreted event. (Doctoral dissertation, Georgetown University, 1989).

Roy, C. (1993). A sociolinguistic analysis of the interpreter's role in simultaneous talk in interpreted interaction. *Multilingua,* 12(4), 341–63.

Wadensjo, C. (1992). *Interpreting as interaction: On dialogue interpreting in immigration and medical encounters.* Linkoping: Linkoping University.

Zimmer, J. (1989). ASL/English interpreting in an interactive setting. In D. Hammond (Ed.), *Proceedings of the 30th annual conference of the American Translators Association.* Medford, NJ: Learned Information.

MEDICAL SETTING 1

This selection is approximately 13 minutes long.

TERMINOLOGY

Write definitions for the following terms before viewing Setting 1.

Otolaryngologist ______________________

____

____

Post nasal drip ______________________

____

____

Nausea ______________________

____

____

Vomiting ______________________________

____

____

Diarrhea ______________________________

____

____

Your past (medical) history ______________________________

____

____

Asthma ______________________________

____

____

Diabetes ______________________________

____

____

High blood pressure ______________________________

____

____

Over-the-counter medicines ______________________________

____

____

Birth control ______________________________

____

____

____

Penicillin ______________________________

____

____

Antibiotic ______________________________

____

____

Lymph nodes ______________________________

____

____

PARTICIPANTS

Physician	Dr. Kathleen Fitch
Patient	Sherina Lee
Interpreter	Holly Peppler

KEY

+	Indicates communication between the interpreter and the doctor.
#	Indicates overlapping spoken utterances.

INTRODUCTIONS

Peppler Hello. My name is Holly Peppler, and I'm an interpreter from the Riverside area. I grew up in a

	hearing family on Long Island, New York, and became an interpreter after college. And that's me.
Dr. Fitch	I'm Dr. Kathleen Fitch. I'm an Otolaryngologist in the San Diego area, and I grew up in La Jolla, California.
Lee	*Please see the accompanying videotext for Ms. Lee's introduction.*

Transcript for MEDICAL SETTING 1

Dr. Fitch	Hi. My name is Dr. Kathleen Fitch. I see you brought an interpreter here with you today.
Interpreter	Yes, I did.
Dr. Fitch	I'm Dr. Fitch.
Interpreter +	Hi, Dr. Fitch. I'm Holly Peppler. Have you worked with an interpreter before?
Dr, Fitch +	No, I haven't.
Interpreter +	A few tips would be: I'll be sitting behind you, and so you won't see me, and she'll be watching me most of the time. You can talk directly to Sherina. You don't have to say, "Tell her" or "Is she?" Just

	talk directly and pretend I'm not here. And don't worry about the lack of eye contact. As hearing people, sometimes we want to have that contact, and hey, hey, hey, look at me. But she'll be watching the interpreter most of the time. Just go ahead and everything will be smooth in a few minutes.
Dr. Fitch +	Great. (To patient) Have you worked with Holly before?
Interpreter	No.
Dr. Fitch	O.K. Fine. Tell me what problem brings you to the office today?
Interpreter	O.K. I have a really sore throat; it's been about a week now.
Dr. Fitch	Do you have any other symptoms of a cold along with the sore throat?
Interpreter	No. No. Just, I've been eating a lot less.
Dr. Fitch	Do you have any fever?
Interpreter	No.
Dr. Fitch	Do you notice any swellings in your neck?
Interpreter	I wouldn't even know how to answer that.

Dr. Fitch	Is your nose normal? Do you have any post-nasal drip or breathing problems?
Interpreter	No. No.
Dr. Fitch	Any nausea, vomiting, or diarrhea?
Interpreter	No. None.
Dr. Fitch	Good. I'm going to ask you about your past history.
Interpreter	O.K.
Dr. Fitch	Do you have any major health problems, for example, asthma, diabetes, high blood pressure?
Interpreter	No. None.
Dr. Fitch	Good. Have you ever had any surgeries?
Interpreter	No.
Dr. Fitch	Are you taking any medicines of any kind right now?
Interpreter	Sort of over-the-counter. Nyquil. Over-the-counter type remedy.
Dr. Fitch	O.K. Do you take birth control pills?
Interpreter	No. No. No.
Dr. Fitch	Are you allergic to any medicines?
Interpreter	Yes, I am. Penicillin.

Dr. Fitch	What kind of a reaction did you have with penicillin?
Interpreter	I just get a rash and swelling. I kind of blow up. In my facial area.
Dr. Fitch	O.K. Do you have to take any antibiotic before you visit the dentist?
Interpreter	No.
Dr. Fitch	Are you married?
Interpreter	Yes, I am.
Dr. Fitch	Do you have any children?
Interpreter	No. No children.
Dr. Fitch	Is your husband or any of your co-workers sick?
Interpreter	Yes. I think that one of my co-workers, the one who gave me this.
Dr. Fitch	I'm going to examine you now, and I do everything in the same order so I don't forget something. And I'm going to look at your ears first.
Interpreter	O.K.
Dr. Fitch	Before I start, though, tell me, have you been deaf from birth, or did you become deaf later?
Interpreter	I became deaf later.
Dr. Fitch	How old were you?

Interpreter	I was three.
Dr. Fitch	Do you have any hearing at all?
Interpreter	Yes, with hearing aids, I'm able to hear.
Dr. Fitch	O.K. Are you wearing them now?
Interpreter	Yes, I am.
Dr. Fitch	O.K. I'm going to have you take them out for a minute while I examine your ears. Then, you can put them right back in.
Interpreter	All right.
Dr. Fitch	Your ears look very good, and you may put your hearings aids back in. Great. I'm going to examine your neck now. Swallow, please. I'm sorry, I know it's very sore. You have some very small lymph nodes that are normal with a sore throat. This is my headlight. I'm going to wear it so I can see better. I'm going to look at your nose first. Your nose looks very good as well. On the inside as well as the outside. I'm going to look in your mouth. Open, please. Great. I'm going to look deeper into your throat. This may cause you to gag a little. Open. Relax your tongue. Good. Next, I'm going to take a throat culture.

This won't feel good on the back of your throat. I apologize in advance, and I'll try to make it as easy as possible. O.K. Open your mouth. Are you O.K.?

Interpreter Yeah.

Dr. Fitch If we're very gentle, we don't get a very good culture. There's a myth that we can tell strep throat by looking at it. And I don't know whether this is strep or not, and that's why I took the culture. You say you've had the infection for a week. Is it getting better or worse?

Interpreter It's becoming worse.

Dr. Fitch When somebody has had an infection for a whole week and it's not getting better, I will treat them, even if the culture is negative. The culture will just help me in case there is another bacteria besides strep. Normally, we'd like to use penicillin for sore throats, but not with you, so I will use erythromycin. Have you had erythromycin before?

Interpreter No, I haven't.

Dr. Fitch Sometimes it can cause an upset stomach, so I will prescribe a little more expensive kind that is less likely to upset your stomach.

Interpreter O.K.

Dr. Fitch I want you to take it three times a day with food.

Interpreter # Oh.

Dr. Fitch # The instructions should be on the bottle. If you have any reaction to the medicine, please call me.

Interpreter # O.K.

Dr. Fitch # If you have a very mild stomachache or very mild diarrhea, put up with it. But anything worse, call me.

Interpreter # O.K.

Dr. Fitch You're not pregnant or trying to get pregnant right now, are you?

Interpreter Huh-uh.

Dr. Fitch This medicine is safe in pregnancy, but I ask all women of child-bearing age that question. Make sure you finish the entire ten days of the medicine.

Interpreter I have to take it every day?

Dr. Fitch Yes, because if you don't, the bacteria may develop a resistance, and the medicine won't be as effective.

Interpreter # Oh. O.K.

Dr. Fitch # And if you stop short, the infection may come back. Let me know if it's not gone at the end of the ten days of antibiotic, or there's any new symptoms that come up.

Interpreter O.K. I will.

Dr. Fitch Do you have any questions or concerns for me?

Interpreter No. No questions.

Dr. Fitch It's been a pleasure meeting you, and please come back if you have any more problems.

Dr. Fitch + Thank you, too.

Interpreter + You're welcome. My pleasure.

Interpreter Thank you.

MEDICAL SETTING 2

This selection is approximately 22 minutes long.

TERMINOLOGY

Write definitions for the following terms before viewing Setting 2.

Sinus infection ____________________

____

____

Stuffy nose ____________________

____

____

Drainage ____________________

____

____

Nausea ____________________

____

____

Vomiting ____________________

____

____

Diarrhea ____________________

____

____

Allergies ____________________

____

____

Major diseases (like asthma, diabetes, high blood pressure) ____________________

____

____

Thyroid ____________________

____

____

Thyroid hormone ____________________

____

____

Cyst ____________________

____

____

Congenital ______________________________

____

____

Nostril ________________________________

____

____

Septal deviation __________________________

____

____

Acid indigestion __________________________

____

____

Symptoms ______________________________

____

____

Virus __________________________________

____

____

Prescription _____________________________

____

____

____

Antibiotic ______________________________

____

____

Infection ____________________

____

____

Gargling ____________________

____

____

____

A course (of medicine) ____________________

____

____

Tylenol ____________________

____

____

Decongestant ____________________

____

____

Advil ____________________

____

____

____

PARTICIPANTS

Physician	Dr. Kathleen Fitch
Patient	Cindi Safford
Interpreter	Holly Peppler

KEY

+	Indicates communication between the interpreter and the doctor.
#	Indicates overlapping spoken utterances.

INTRODUCTIONS

Peppler Hello. My name is Holly Peppler, and I'm an interpreter from the Riverside area. I grew up in a hearing family on Long Island, New York, and became an interpreter after college. And that's me.

Dr. Fitch I'm Dr. Kathleen Fitch. I'm an Otolaryngologist in the San Diego area, and I grew up in La Jolla, California.

Safford *Please see the accompanying videotext for Ms. Safford's introduction.*

Transcript for MEDICAL SETTING 2

Dr. Fitch Hello, my name is Dr. Kathleen Fitch. I am an otolaryngologist, or ear, nose and throat surgery.

Interpreter	Hello. My name is Cindi, and I'm here with a sinus kind of infection headache.
Dr. Fitch	How long have you had the sinus infection?
Interpreter	Since last Friday night. It's been ongoing for about three days.
Dr. Fitch	Have you had many sinus infections in the past?
Interpreter	No. It just depends on the weather. If it's cold and hot, and cold and hot, and there's a lot of changeability, then I do tend to get sinus infections.
Dr. Fitch	What symptoms do you have of this sinus infection? For example, stuffy nose, drainage?
Interpreter	This area, I get drainage and I get drainage from this area into my throat. Sometimes I have a lot of drainage in my nose.
Dr. Fitch	What color is the drainage?
Interpreter	Sometimes it's green. Sometimes it's clear.
Dr. Fitch	Do you have any fever with your infection?
Interpreter	No, I'm Just exceedingly tired. I want to sleep all day. I have really low energy.

Dr. Fitch Do you have a cough?

Interpreter No.

Dr. Fitch Do you have a stuffy nose?

Interpreter Yes.

Dr. Fitch Is your nose normally stuffy, or just with this infection?

Interpreter You mean during the sinus infection? Yes, I have one. But sometimes, my ears are sort of all crinkly, crackly. They feel like they have fluid or something in them.

Dr. Fitch Does it feel like you're in an airplane?

Interpreter Exactly.

Dr. Fitch Do you blow your nose a lot?

Interpreter Not really a lot. No.

Dr. Fitch Do you have any nausea, vomiting, or diarrhea?

Interpreter Sometimes. Depends on how bad the infection is. Most times, it'd be diarrhea.

Dr. Fitch Do you have allergies? For example, to dust, molds, animals?

Interpreter No.

Dr. Fitch Let me ask you about your social life. Do you have any children, in particular?

Interpreter	Oh, yes. I have one. I have a four-year-old son.
Dr. Fitch	Is he sick as well?
Interpreter	No, but he has ongoing ear infections.
Dr. Fitch	Are you married?
Interpreter	I'm in the process of a divorce.
Dr. Fitch	So, you're under a lot of stress right now, as well.
Interpreter	No, not really. My ex-husband and I are on very friendly terms.
Dr. Fitch	Good.
Interpreter	A very friendly divorce.
Dr. Fitch	Good. What types of medical problems have you had in the past? Do you have any major diseases like asthma, diabetes, high blood pressure?
Interpreter	I take daily medication for thyroid.
Dr. Fitch	Do you know the name of it?
Interpreter	Synthroid, I believe.
Dr. Fitch	Good. Do you have a doctor who checks it regularly, meaning at least once a year?
Interpreter	You're talking about the thyroid?
Dr. Fitch	Your thyroid hormone level in your body, a blood test.

Interpreter	Yes, once a year. Yes, every year.
Dr. Fitch	That's perfect. Do you take any other medicines?
Interpreter	No.
Dr. Fitch	Are you allergic to any medicines?
Interpreter	No. Uh-uh.
Dr. Fitch	Does anybody in your family, meaning brothers or sisters or parents, have any history of allergies or sinus problems?
Interpreter	My dad has sinus infections, and he had nose/nasal surgery.
Dr. Fitch	Have you ever had any surgeries?
Interpreter	Yes, I have.
Dr. Fitch	What surgeries have you had?
Interpreter	Well, I had a thyroid surgery. There was a cyst on my thighbone . . .
Interpreter +	I'm sorry.
Interpreter	A cyst on my tailbone.
Dr. Fitch	And what was the thyroid surgery for?
Interpreter	For an enlarged thyroid.
Dr. Fitch	Good. Benign disease?
Interpreter	Yes.
Dr. Fitch	I am going to examine you in a minute.
Interpreter	Fine.

Dr. Fitch	I always examine in the same order, so I don't forget anything.
Interpreter	All right.
Dr. Fitch +	How long have you been an interpreter?
Interpreter +	It's best if you speak with the patient directly, or the whole process gets a little bit skewed. We can talk about this, perhaps, after.
Dr. Fitch +	O.K. Thank you.
Dr. Fitch	I'm going to look in your ears first. Now I know you're deaf. Do you have any hearing at all?
Interpreter	Absolutely none. Nothing. I am deaf.
Dr. Fitch	And was the cause of your deafness congenital, or did you get it after birth?
Interpreter	My parents don't know. They didn't know I was deaf until I was three years old. So they really don't know the cause.
Dr. Fitch	I'm going to examine you now. I do everything in the same order to make sure I remember to look at everything.
Interpreter	That's great.

Dr. Fitch	And I'm going to start with your ears. The right ear first. It looks very normal. Your left ear looks a little stuffy but not bad.
Interpreter	Stuffy. What does that look like?
Dr. Fitch	Like when you're on an airplane. That feeling is what you should feel. When I look in your right ear.
Dr. Fitch +	I'm sorry. Were you in the middle of something?
Interpreter +	No. Go ahead. That's fine.
Dr. Fitch	O.K. In the right ear, it sort of looks like a nice pillow puffed out. In the left ear, it looks like somebody just sat on the pillow, and it's not so puffed out. And it's typical of somebody who has a cold or sinus infection.
Interpreter	Oh. Huh.
Dr. Fitch	I'm going to feel your neck next. Swallow please. Was the whole thyroid removed?
Interpreter	No. One-fourth, I believe.
Dr. Fitch	Swallow again. Can't feel much of anything on your thyroid, but that's good. Your neck feels perfect.
Interpreter	Good.

Dr. Fitch This is a bright light. Next, I'm going to look in your nose. This instrument just spreads your nostrils. Try to relax.

Interpreter Uh-huh.

Dr. Fitch Very good. I'm going to look in your mouth next. Everything looks very good. I have two more looks to do in your mouth. Just keep your tongue in your mouth. That examines the part of her throat behind her nose.

Dr. Fitch + The next exam is to look at her vocal cords. I'll have her stick out her tongue, and I'll hold it. And I need her to say the letter "a." Very good, way out. "A."

Safford Aaaah.

Dr. Fitch + Tell her, despite her coughing, I actually got a good look.

Interpreter + Excuse me. You can talk directly to her, if you want.

Dr. Fitch + Thank you.

Dr Fitch Your nose looks very good, except the middle wall is a little crooked, to your right. That is called a septal deviation. You may have heard about people having septal deviations.

Interpreter	No.
Dr. Fitch	Some people with a little crookedness to the middle wall have breathing in their nose because of it.
Interpreter	What would cause that? . . . What would cause me to have that?
Dr. Fitch	You could have been born with it, or you most likely, you were hit sometime in your youth or childhood. You may not even remember it.
Interpreter	I was hit. I did. I ran into a door, probably when I was about 11 years old. Can you do anything about it?
Dr. Fitch	If a person cannot breathe because of it, we have a nice surgery for it. However . . .
Dr Fitch +	Can you speak just a little bit when you sign, so I know when you're done.
Interpreter +	Sure.
Dr. Fitch	When I asked you if you had problems breathing through your nose normally when you don't have an infection, you said, "No." So I wouldn't do anything about it at this time.

Interpreter	Ah. O.K.
Dr. Fitch	I just wanted to make you aware of it.
Interpreter	O.K. So I guess I don't have to worry about it in the future is what you're saying?
Dr. Fitch	Not at all. Not at all. But if you start having problems year-round with breathing through your nose, then we might reconsider that. I see many patients with deviated septums, and only a small percentage do I ever operate on.
Interpreter	Now, how often should I have that checked, do you suppose?
Dr. Fitch	Never, unless it's causing you problems.
Interpreter	Oh, O.K.
Dr. Fitch	Do you have a sore throat at all?
Interpreter	Now?
Dr. Fitch	Yes.
Interpreter	No.
Dr. Fitch	How's your stomach? Do you get acid indigestion?
Interpreter	No. It's fine. Why?
Dr. Fitch	Your vocal cords, the back ends are just a little bit red.

Interpreter	Huh. No. I don't feel sick, except for this sinus infection.
Dr. Fitch	This is the type of sign that if you have no symptoms, I don't give it any importance, but if you had symptoms, then I would interpret it differently.
Interpreter	Oh. O.K. Huh.
Dr. Fitch	I don't see any drainage, any redness, any green or yellow at this particular minute.
Interpreter	Great. O.K.
Dr. Fitch	You have a very mild virus—or you have a virus with a very beginning of a bacterial or sinus infection.
Interpreter	Uh, huh. So, should I have medicine for that to prevent it from becoming worse? Or. . . .
Dr. Fitch	At this point, I think you're better off doing all the things your mom told you to do. Get plenty of rest.
Interpreter	Water. Salt.
Dr. Fitch	Yes. Drink plenty of fluids. Get plenty of rest. Don't overdo it. And it should be gone by the end of this next week. However, if it gets worse and it turns green

	or yellow, and it stays that way consistently for several days, or it doesn't go away after a week's time, call my office, and I will call in a prescription for an antibiotic for you.
Interpreter	All right.
Dr. Fitch	If I give you an antibiotic, it should work within a couple days. You should feel better after a couple days. However, you will not feel like the infection is gone for about a week. We usually give 10 days of an antibiotic.
Interpreter #	Um, hum. Great.
Dr. Fitch #	Because after 10 days, most people are cured. The last . . .
Interpreter #	Should I take that with water, or the salt in the water—should I have that, like a gargling?
Dr. Fitch	If you don't have a sore throat, you don't need salt water for your throat. However, if you'd like to spray some or squirt some in your nose, that's fine. That might help your nose feel a little better.
Interpreter	O.K. All right.
Dr. Fitch	Back to the antibiotic. You should be taking the last few days,

because I told you so, but you feel like you're better and you really didn't need to take them, but you're a good patient, and you do what the doctor says.

Interpreter I'm aware of having to take them.

Dr. Fitch I'm telling you this, because if you don't follow this particular course, I need you to call the office back and tell us you're not getting well. Most of the time, the antibiotic we choose works great, but sometimes we pick the wrong one. In the meantime, any medicine you want to take for symptoms, for example, Tylenol for aches or pains, or a decongestant to help you breathe at night, is fine.

Interpreter Right now, I'm taking Advil instead of Tylenol, because I've noticed that Tylenol doesn't tend to make me feel better. Is that all right?

Dr. Fitch That's perfect.

Interpreter Great.

Dr. Fitch Do you have any questions for me before we're done?

Interpreter	Well, since you said something about my left ear, do I have to worry about that?
Dr. Fitch	No. That is just a sign to me that what you're telling me about your ears crackling and popping is consistent. That should go away when your infection goes away, and it's a very minor problem.
Interpreter	O.K. Great.
Dr. Fitch	Do you intend to travel on an airplane anytime in the next couple weeks?
Interpreter	No. Well, I hope not.
Dr. Fitch	Good. That's the only time that ear might give you trouble, if you were to take a plane today. You might have a little pain.
Interpreter	What about swimming? Can I go in the water? Because I have a pool at home. Can I swim?
Dr. Fitch	I don't want you doing a lot of exercise. You can do a very mild amount of exercise, and you can certainly float in the pool, or be with your son for a short period.
Interpreter	Darn it. O.K., No, fine.
Dr. Fitch	Anything else?
Interpreter	No. I think that's it. Thank you.

Dr. Fitch	It's been a pleasure meeting you.
Interpreter	Same here.
Dr. Fitch	And remember to call the office if you're not getting better.
Interpreter	O.K., I will.

MEDICAL SETTING 3

This selection is approximately 6 minutes long.

TERMINOLOGY

Write definitions for the following terms before viewing Setting 3.

Crowns ______________________________

____

____

Entail ______________________________

____

____

Root canal ______________________________

____

____

Orthodontics ______________________________

____

____

Braces (in the context of orthodontics) __________

____

____

PARTICIPANTS

Dentist	Dennis Huston
Patient	Mary Vu
Interpreter	Sue Eadie
Dental Assistant	Sara Moraz

KEY

+	Indicates communication between the interpreter and the doctor.
#	Indicates overlapping spoken utterances.

INTRODUCTIONS

Dr. Huston My name is Dr. Dennis Huston, and I've been a practicing dentist in the San Diego area for the last 22 years.

Eadie	My name is Sue Eadie. I'm a certified sign language interpreter. I've been interpreting since 1976, and I live in Oakland, California.
Sara Moraz	Hi, my name is Sara Moraz and I'm a dental assistant in San Diego, California.
Vu	*Please see the accompanying videotext for Ms. Vu's introduction.*

Transcript for MEDICAL SETTING 3

Dr. Huston	Good morning, Mary. We're glad to see you in the office today. We understand from what you have told our receptionist that you are having some problems with your teeth, and we wanted to see if we can go ahead and have you explain that to us, and perhaps we can help you with that.
Interpreter	I'm having a problem with an infection. When I eat ice or I drink something cold, it's very sensitive. And also when I eat hot foods, it's sensitive, too. It's hard. About a year ago, I had new crowns put on. But I'm wondering if you can

help me with this infection, if you can find out what's going on.

Dr. Huston O.K. Mary, it's fairly common to have some sensitivity with new crowns, but if it's been ongoing for a year, I would tend to worry a little bit that there may be something happening to the nerve of the tooth. And so, I think it would be best if we went ahead and took an x-ray, and I can check that way to see if there, in fact, is something happening down in the nerve of the tooth.

Interpreter + If you're going to do an x-ray, is there some kind of protective clothing that I can use, or can I leave the room?

Dr. Huston + Yes, we can do either. I've got a shield that you can wear, the same as what we'll give the patient. Or, if you want, you can leave the room when we place the x-ray. It only takes a fraction of a second to take that.

Interpreter + I think I would like to leave the room during the x-ray, so that I'm not exposed to that, if you don't mind. Is that O.K. with you? That's O.K. with her. So, let's do that.

Dr. Huston O.K. Fine. We'll just exit this way, and then we'll have Sara come in and take the x-ray in just a moment.

Interpreter O.K.

Sara Moraz taking x-ray.

Dr. Huston Mary, I had a chance to take a look at the x-ray that Sara just took for us, and you were correct. It does seem that there is an infection that's starting in one of those teeth that you had the crowns done on. So I wanted to go ahead and see if we can find time to take care of that for you, take care of the infection. Now, let me explain what that's going to entail for us. What we're going to need to do is do a root canal. What that means is that we leave the crown in place, but we do make a small hole in the back of the crown, and we take the nerve out and, at the same time, we take the infection out. We will seal that off, and that will take care of a lot of the symptoms and the sensitivity that you've been having. My receptionist also told me that you weren't very pleased with how the crowns looked, and I wanted to find out exactly what the problem was and let's see if we can address that also.

Interpreter I'm not happy with the way they look. They feel like they're too big, and also, of course, the infection, the pain, you know. I feel like they stick out too much, and I want them to be more flat and closer to my mouth. So I want you to help me change my crowns. Maybe take them all off or redo them, I'm not sure.

Dr. Huston O.K. There are only two ways that we can change the looks and the appearance of the crowns. One is to do, as you talked about, which is take the crowns off and remake them and try to make them thinner. That doesn't always work, because if we make them too thin, the color doesn't look right. The second option would be to actually have the teeth moved. This is called orthodontics, and for that, all we would want to do is actually have them place braces on your teeth and move those into a better position. And those are the two ways that we can go ahead and repair what you feel is not an acceptable result for you. So, what I would do is I would go ahead and at this point, let's take care of the pain. Let's take care of the part that's making it difficult for you to chew and eat. And, once we're certain that everything is comfortable for you, at that point, then we can go ahead and see about changing how the teeth look.

Interpreter O.K.

Dr. Huston All right. What let's do then, let's go ahead, and we'll make an appointment for sometime in the next week, and we can start the process of taking care of that infection for you.

Interpreter O.K.

Dr. Huston O.K.? Good.